Just to let you know...

A message from _____

Help your child discover the joy of independent reading with **SRA *Imagine It!*** From time to time your child will bring home his or her very own *Pre-Decodable Takehomes* to share with you. With your help, these stories can give your child important reading practice and a joyful shared reading experience.

You may want to set aside a few minutes every evening to read these stories together. Here are some suggestions you may find helpful:

- Do not expect your child to read each story perfectly, but concentrate on sharing the book together.
- Participate by doing some of the reading.
- Talk about the stories as you read, give lots of encouragement, and watch as your child becomes more fluent throughout the year!

Learning to read takes lots of practice. Sharing these stories is one way that your child can gain that valuable practice. Encourage your child to keep the *Pre-Decodable Takehomes* in a special place. This collection will make a library of books that your child can read and reread. Take the time to listen to your child read from his or her library. Just a few moments of shared reading each day can give your child the confidence needed to excel in reading.

Children who read every day come to think of reading as a pleasant, natural part of life. One way to inspire your child to read is to show that reading is an important part of your life by letting him or her see you reading books, magazines, newspapers, or any other materials. Another good way to show that you value reading is to share a *Pre-Decodable Takehome* with your child each day.

Successful reading experiences allow children to be proud of their new-found reading ability. Support your child with interest and enthusiasm about reading. You won't regret it!

Pre-Decodable Takehomes

Level Pre-K

Pre-Decodables 1–20

SRA

Columbus, OH

SRAonline.com

 SRA

Send all inquiries to this address:
SRA/McGraw-Hill
4400 Easton Commons
Columbus, OH 43219-6188

ISBN: 978-0-07-617042-5
MHID: 0-07-617042-X

   4 5 6 7 8 9 WDQ 14 13 12 11 10

Contents

About the Pre-Decodable Takehomes

The **SRA Imagine It!** *Pre-Decodables* allow your students to apply their knowledge of high-frequency words to read simple, engaging texts. Each story supports instruction in a new high-frequency word and incorporates words that have been learned earlier.

The students can fold and staple the pages of each *Pre-Decodable Takehome* to make books of their own to keep and read. We suggest that you keep extra sets of the stories in your classroom for the children to reread.

How to Make a Takehome

1. Tear out the pages you need.

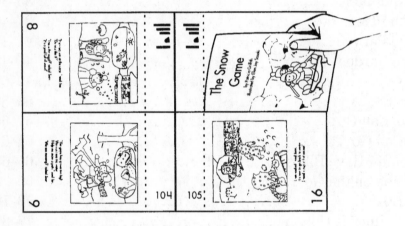

2. Place pages 4 and 5, and pages 2 and 7 faceup.

3. Place pages 4 and 5 on top of pages 2 and 7.

4. Fold along the center line.

5. Check to make sure the pages are in order.

6. Staple the pages along the fold.

SRA Pre-Decodables

Grandma's Visit

by Connie Williams
illustrated by Carol Heyer

Pre-Decodable 1

SRA

Columbus, OH

SRAonline.com

SRA

All rights reserved. The contents, or parts thereof, may be reproduced in print form for non-profit educational use with *Imagine It!* provided such reproductions bear copyright notice, but may not be reproduced in any form for any other purpose without the prior written consent of The McGraw-Hill Companies, Inc., including, but not limited to, network storage or transmission, or broadcast for distance learning. An Open Court Curriculum.

Printed in the United States of America.

Send all inquiries to this address:
SRA/McGraw-Hill
4400 Easton Commons
Columbus, OH 43219

SRA Pre-Decodables

A

Family

by Seamus Waibel
illustrated by Gary Undercuffler

Pre-Decodable 2

SRA

Columbus, OH

a

family

The McGraw-Hill Companies

a

baby

a

boy

a

father

4

a

girl

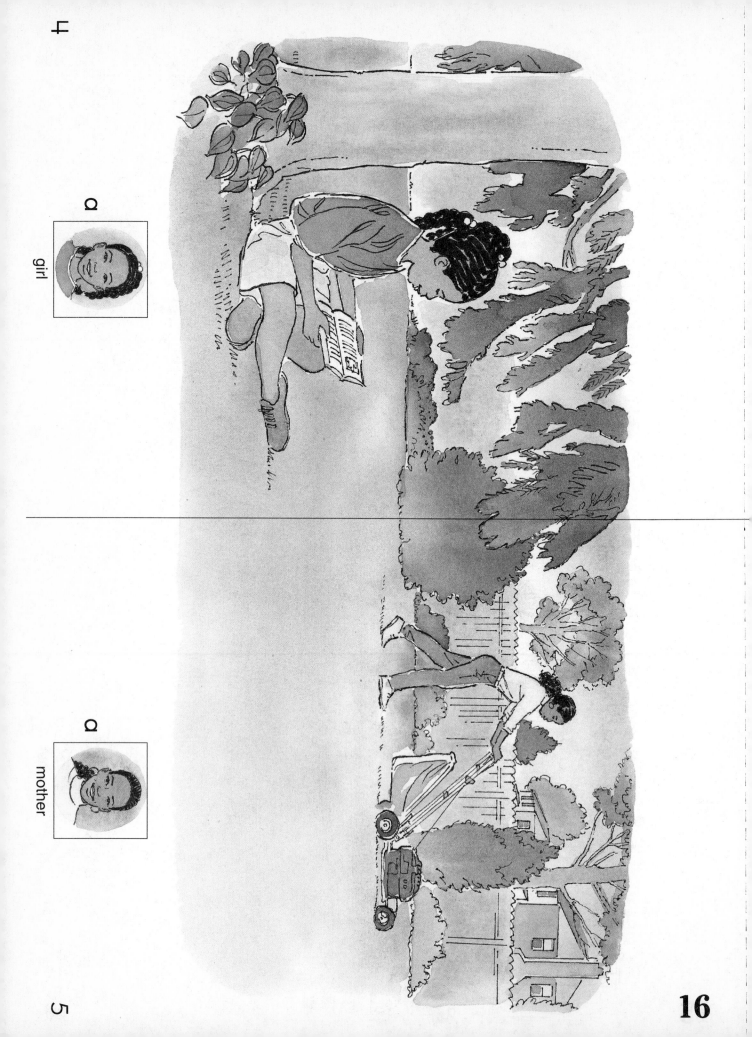

a

mother

5

16

SRA Pre-Decodables

Picnic

The

by Radley Womack
illustrated by Meryl Henderson

Pre-Decodable 3

McGraw Hill SRA

Columbus, OH

a

family

the uncles

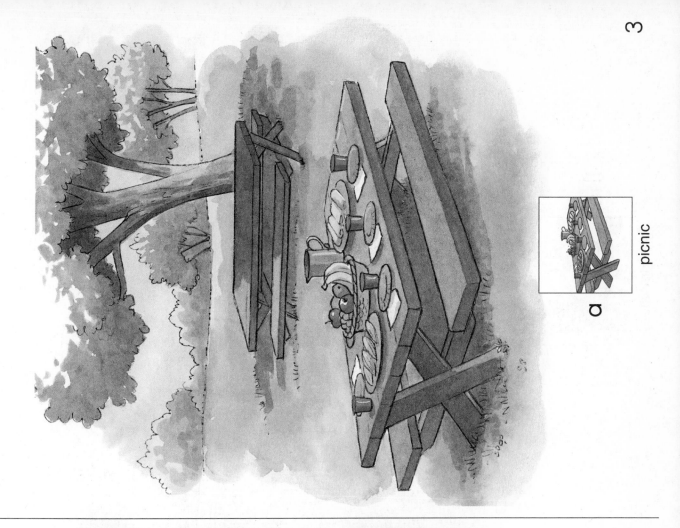

a

picnic

the

aunts

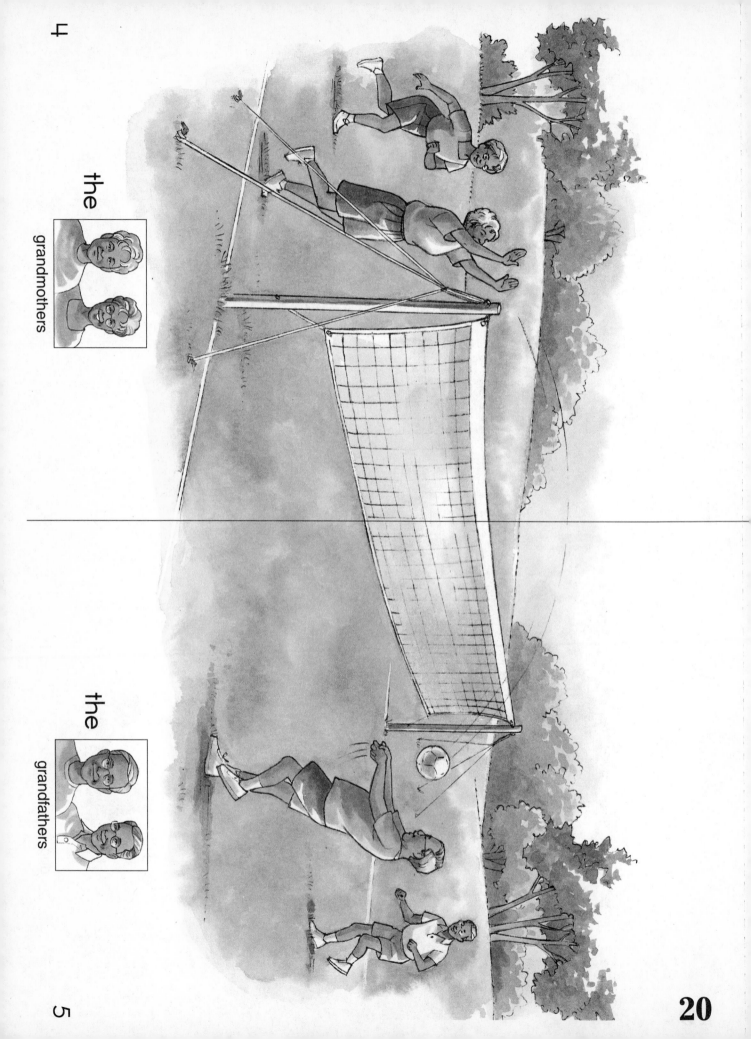

4

the

grandmothers

the

grandfathers

5

20

SRA Pre-Decodables

Friends

by Ellenor Gray
illustrated by Susan Jaekel

Pre-Decodable 4

 SRA

Columbus, OH

the [dog] and the [cat]

dog   cat

SRAonline.com

Mc
Graw
Hill

SRA

Printed in the United States of America.

Send all inquiries to this address:
SRA/McGraw-Hill
4400 Easton Commons
Columbus, OH 43219

the

boy

and the

teddy bear

a **boy** and a **girl**

the and the

the **girl** and the **doll**

4

a 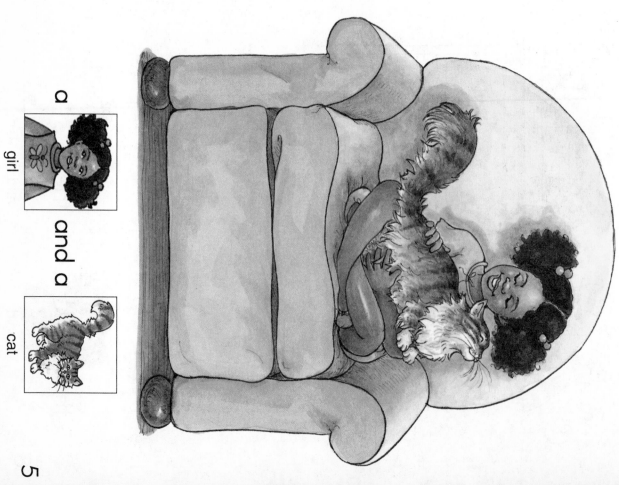 boy and a dog

5

a girl and a cat

24

SRA Pre-Decodables

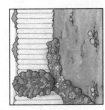

In the Yard

by Max Caesar
illustrated by Loretta Lustig

Pre-Decodable 5

Mc Graw Hill **SRA**

Columbus, OH

in the

yard

8

25

SRAonline.com

Mc Graw Hill

SRA

Printed in the United States of America.

Send all inquiries to this address:
SRA/McGraw-Hill
4400 Easton Commons
Columbus, OH 43219

in a

box

in ☐ and ☐
grass   flowers

the ☐ and the ☐
cat   flowers

4

in the

flowers

in a

washtub

5

28

SRA Pre-Decodables

Helpers

by Rachel Turner
illustrated by Jon Goodell

Pre-Decodable 6

Mc Graw Hill **SRA**

Columbus, OH

on the ☐ ladder

SRAonline.com

Mc
Graw
Hill
SRA

Printed in the United States of America.

Send all inquiries to this address:
SRA/McGraw-Hill
4400 Easton Commons
Columbus, OH 43219

in a

car

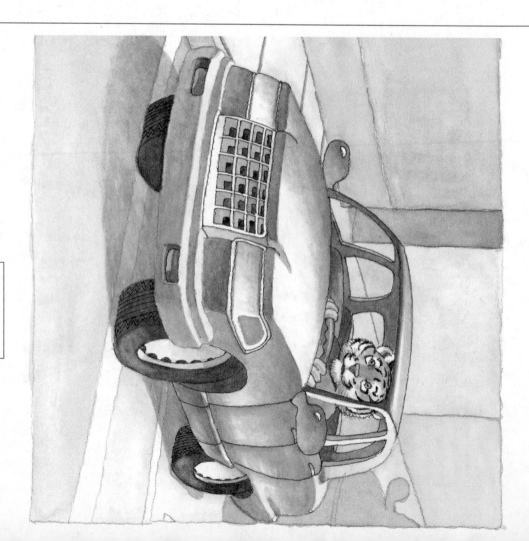

on the 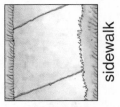 sidewalk

on a  street

31

on a

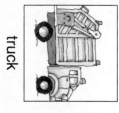

truck

in a

truck

SRA Pre-Decodables

A
Firefighter

by Zachary Norris
illustrated by Dennis Hockerman

Pre-Decodable 7

Mc Graw Hill **SRA**

Columbus, OH

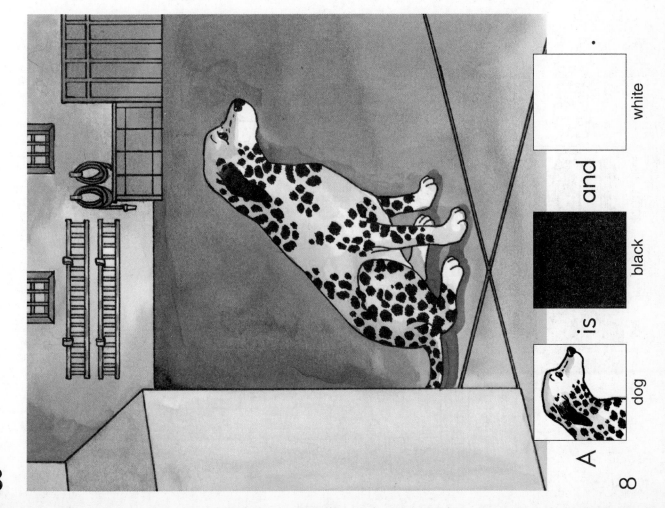

A dog is black and white .

33

8

SRAonline.com

SRA
Mc Graw Hill

Copyright © 2008 by SRA/McGraw-Hill.

Printed in the United States of America.

Send all inquiries to this address:
SRA/McGraw-Hill
4400 Easton Commons
Columbus, OH 43219

The McGraw-Hill Companies

2

A [fire truck] is [   ] .

fire truck   red

34

7

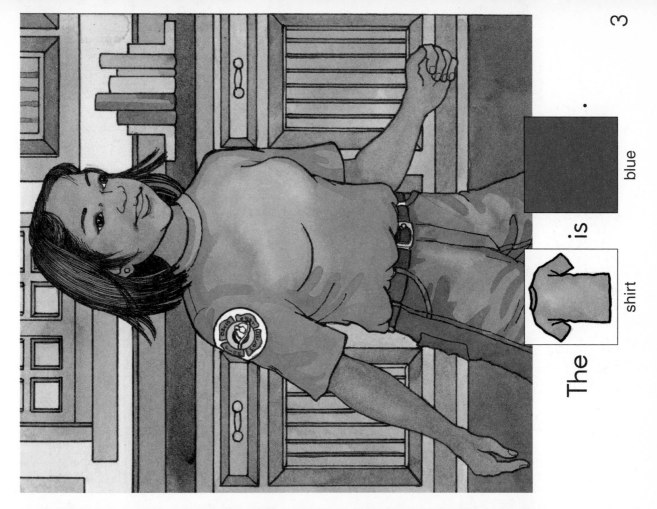

The is [ ].

shirt   blue

The  is [ ].

hat   black

4

The 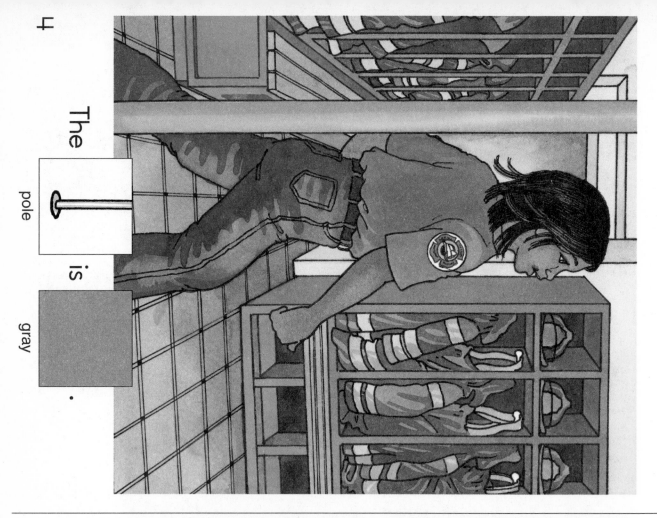 is _____ .

pole   gray

The 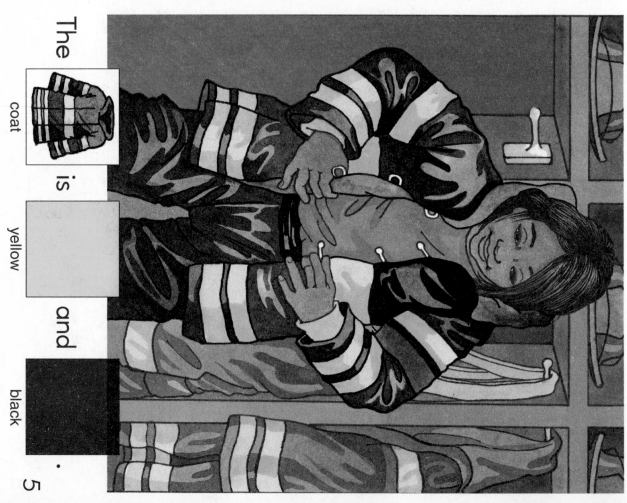 is _____ and _____ .

coat   yellow   black

5

36

SRA Pre-Decodables

Tree

See the

by Meredith Sanchez
illustrated by Len Ebert

Pre-Decodable 8

SRA

Columbus, OH

See a green

tree.

See on the 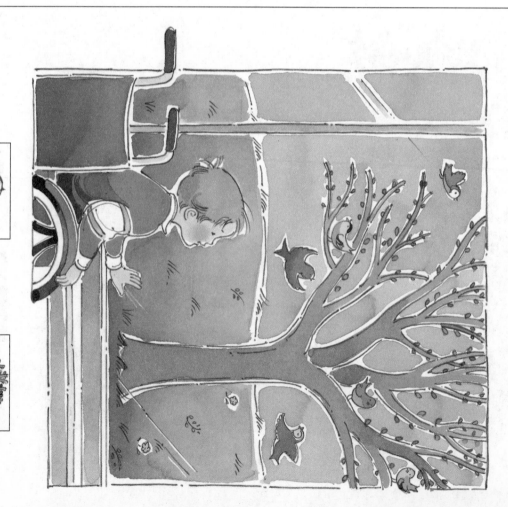 .

birds

tree

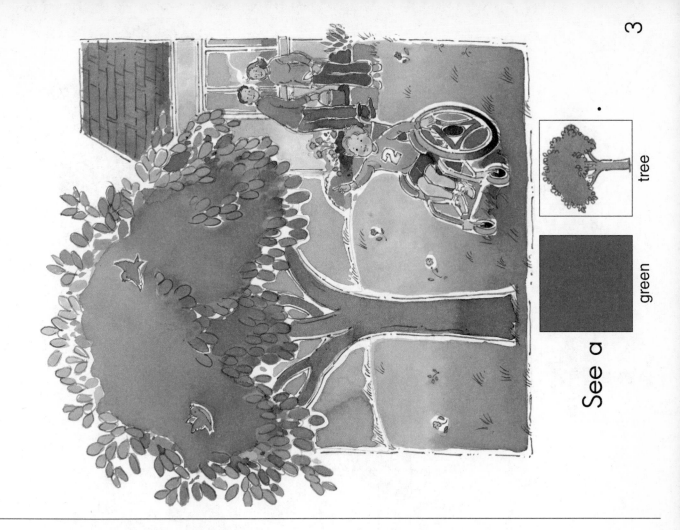

See a green ☐
green   tree

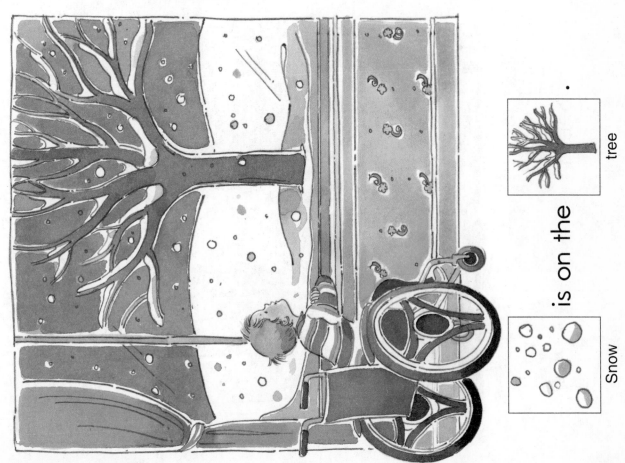

Snow is on the .
Snow   tree

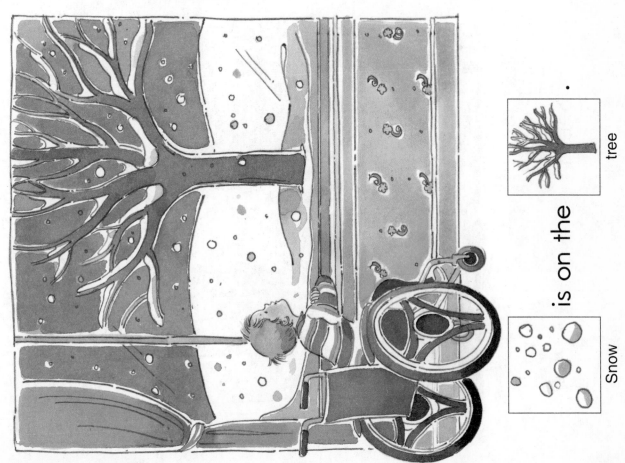

4

A

bird

is on the

tree

.

5

See a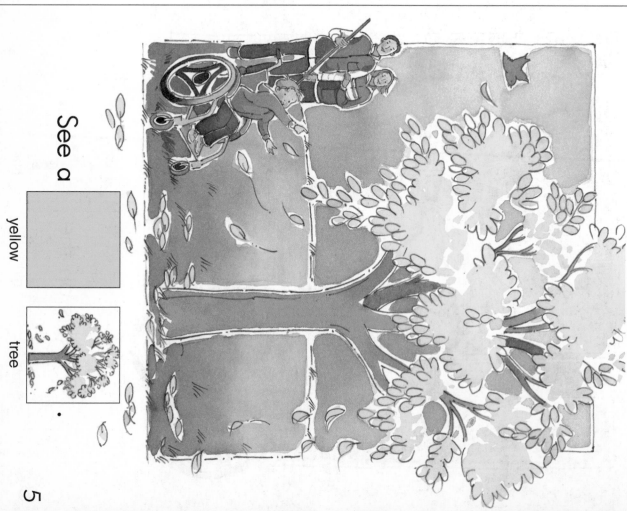

yellow

tree

.

SRA Pre-Decodables

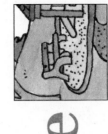

At the Park

by David Powell
illustrated by Susan Lexa

Pre-Decodable 9

Mc Graw Hill SRA

Columbus, OH

See the

girl

sled

2

See the

girl

at the

hill

.

7

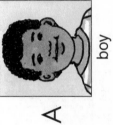

A 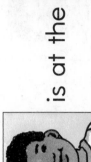 is at the .

boy   park

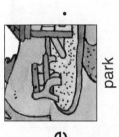

A 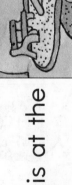 is at the  .

girl   park

4

See the 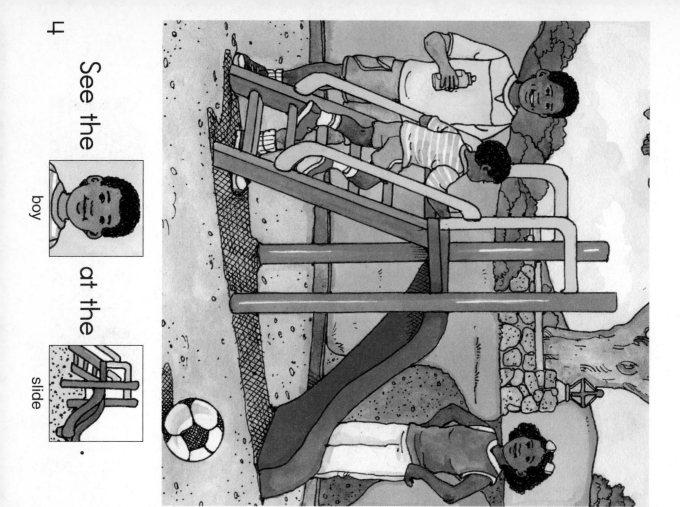 at the .

boy   slide

5

See the 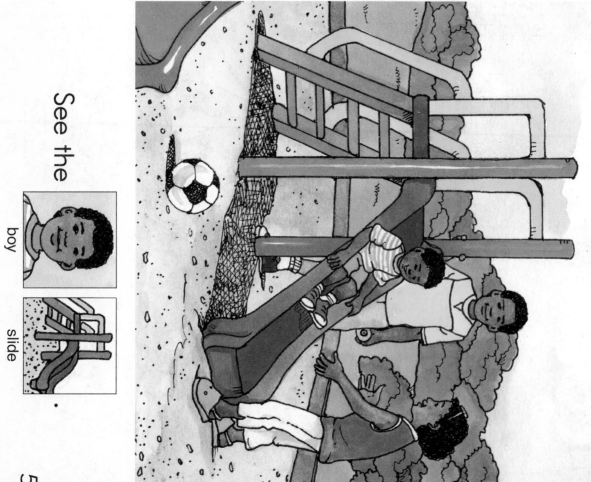 .

boy   slide

44

I  hug Mom.

SRA Pre-Decodables

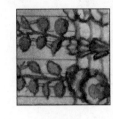 Garden

In the

by Harriet Nisely
illustrated by Angela Adams

Pre-Decodable 10

Mc Graw Hill SRA

Columbus, OH

SRAonline.com

Mc Graw Hill

SRA

The McGraw-Hill Companies

I taste in the garden .

I  hear birds in trees .

3

47

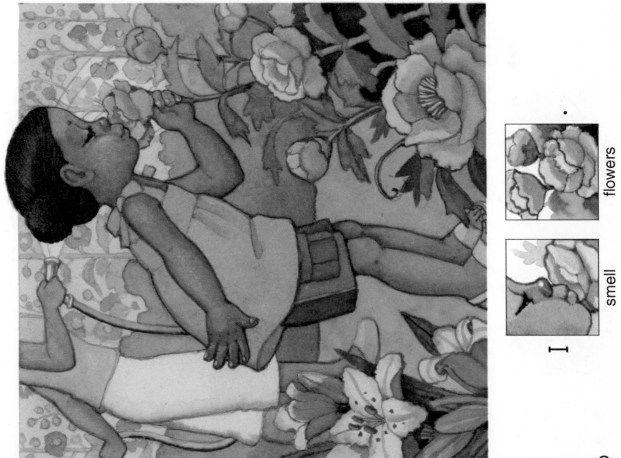

I smell flowers .

6

4

I see 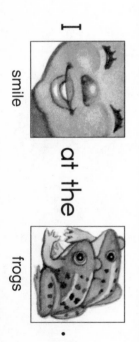 at the .

frogs

pond

5

I at the .

smile

frogs

48

SRA Pre-Decodables

I Have

by Lindsey Miller
illustrated by Lorinda Bryan Cauley

Pre-Decodable 11

SRA

Columbus, OH

I have a ▢ .

tongue

and I have

2 two

feet .

I have a 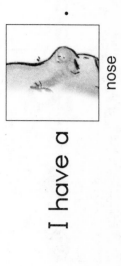 .

nose

I have 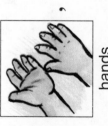 2 hands ,

two

51

I have

2
two

eyes ,

and I have

2
two

ears .

SRA Pre-Decodables

I Can See

by Calvin Roberts
illustrated by Diane Paterson

Pre-Decodable 12

 Mc Graw Hill **SRA**

Columbus, OH

The [bird] can [bird] sing.

SRAonline.com

Mc Graw Hill   **SRA**

Copyright © 2008 by SRA/McGraw-Hill.

All rights reserved. The contents, or parts thereof, may be reproduced in print form for non-profit educational use with *Imagine It!* provided such reproductions bear copyright notice, but may not be reproduced in any form for any other purpose without the prior written consent of The McGraw-Hill Companies, Inc., including, but not limited to, network storage or transmission, or broadcast for distance learning. An Open Court Curriculum.

Printed in the United States of America.

Send all inquiries to this address:
SRA/McGraw-Hill
4400 Easton Commons
Columbus, OH 43219

I can see a

bird

.

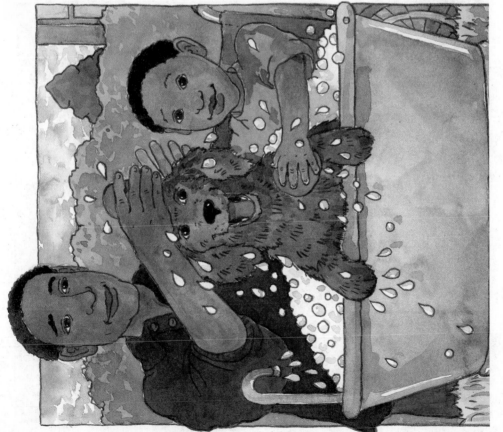

The  can have a  .

dog

bath

6

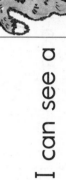

I can see a .

cat

3

55

4

The  can have a  .

cat   ball

I can see a  .

dog

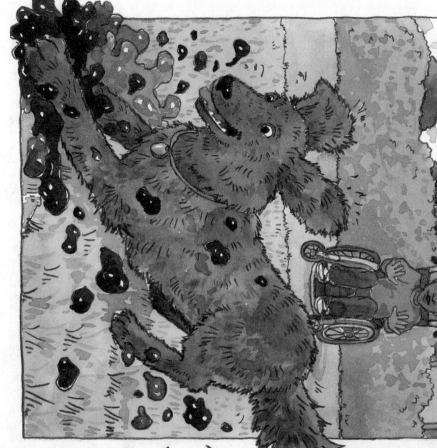

5

56

SRA Pre-Decodables

Can Go

Bears

by Robin Gillig
illustrated by Nicole Rutten

Pre-Decodable 13

Mc Graw Hill **SRA**

Columbus, OH

go in the

pool

Bears

57

SRAonline.com

Mc Graw Hill SRA

Printed in the United States of America.

Send all inquiries to this address:
SRA/McGraw-Hill
4400 Easton Commons
Columbus, OH 43219

Bears

can go on a

slide .

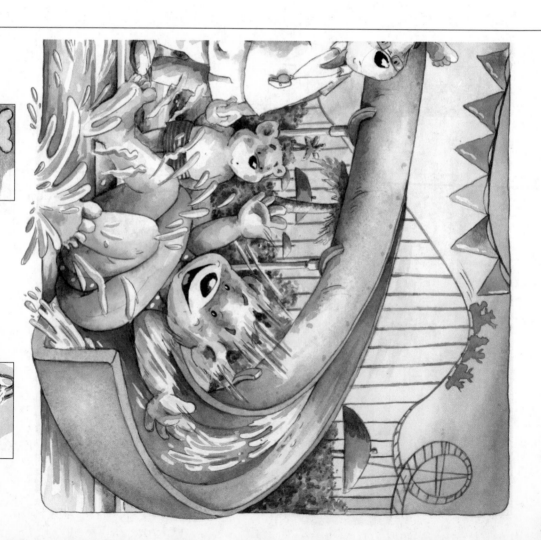

Bears go on bikes

Bears can go up steps

4

Bears

go in

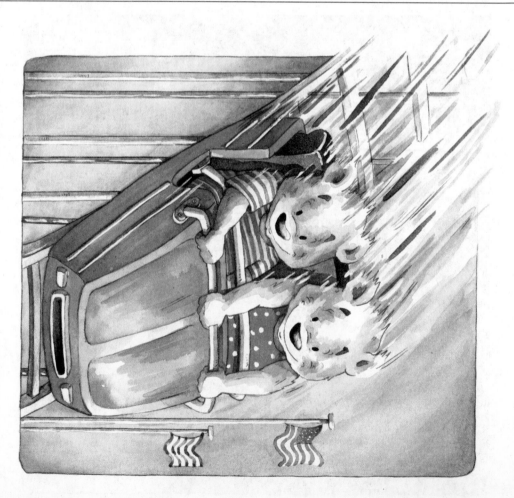

boats

.

5

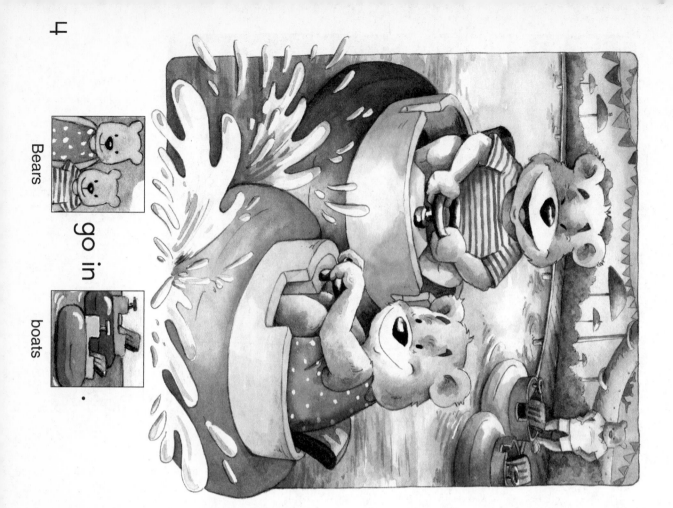

Bears

go on a

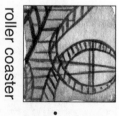

roller coaster

.

SRA Pre-Decodables

She Can Go

by Kevin Richards
illustrated by Meryl Henderson

Pre-Decodable 14

SRA

Columbus, OH

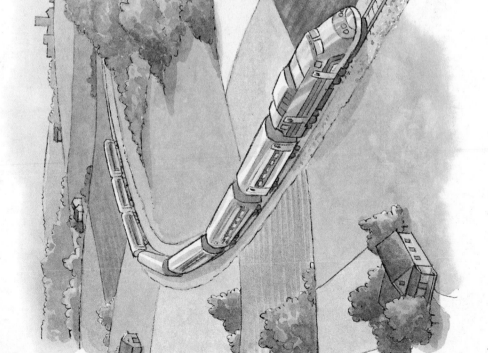

61

The  can go.

train

SRAonline.com

Mc
Graw
Hill

SRA

She can see

trees

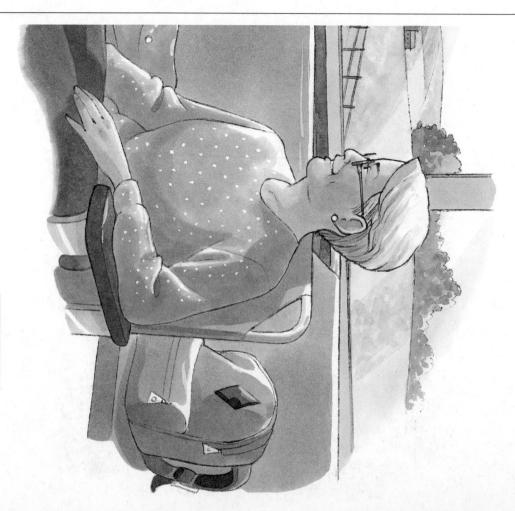

.

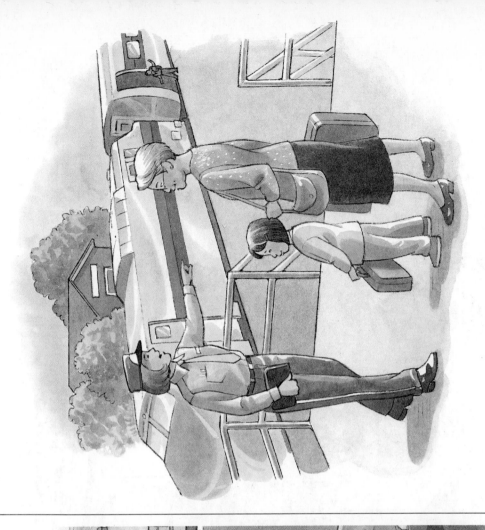

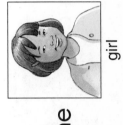

girl

The ____ can go.

She can see a ____ .

farm

4

She is in a

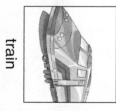

seat

.

She is on the

train

.

5

64

SRA Pre-Decodables

You and I Have

Bikes

by Kristen John
illustrated by Len Ebert

Pre-Decodable 15

SRA

Columbus, OH

You and I can go.

65

8

You and I have

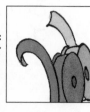
ribbons .

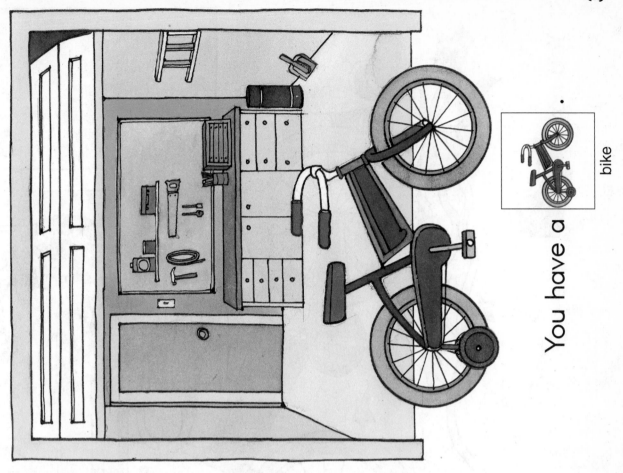

You have a _____ .

bike

3

You and I have _____ .

bikes

4 You have

tape

and

scissors

.

You have

ribbons

.

5

68

SRA Pre-Decodables

She Was on the Go

by Will Kemper
illustrated by Kristen Goeters

Pre-Decodable 16

Mc Graw Hill SRA

Columbus, OH

69

At **5** , she was on .

five

skates

8

At **4** , she was on a .

four

bike

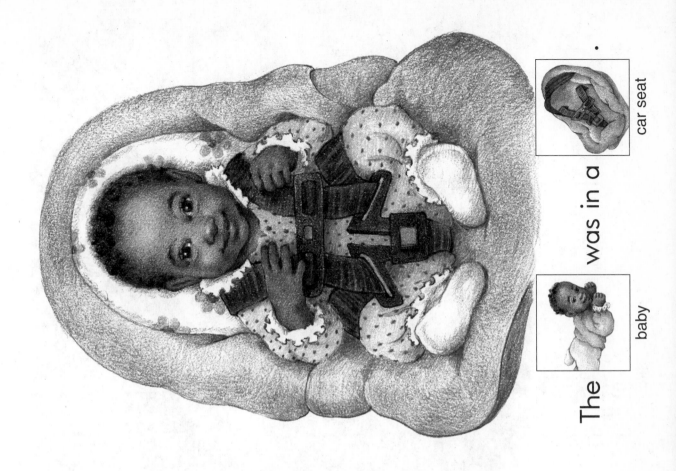

The  was in a  .

baby   car seat

At **3** , she was in a .

three   wagon

At **1**

one

, she was in a

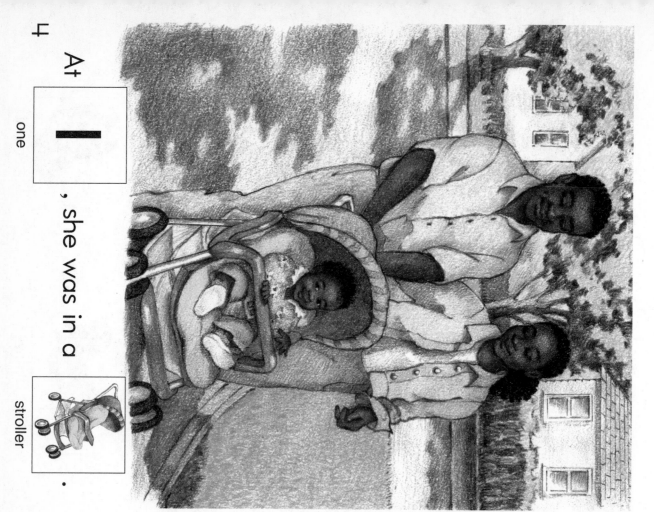

. stroller

At **2**

two

, she was in a

. car

4

5

72

SRA Pre-Decodables

The 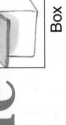 Box

by Jacqueline Young
illustrated by Jane McCreary

Pre-Decodable 17

McGraw Hill SRA

Columbus, OH

The  house was a  box

with a door .

SRAonline.com

SRA

Printed in the United States of America.

Send all inquiries to this address:
SRA/McGraw-Hill
4400 Easton Commons
Columbus, OH 43219

You and I have a .

bus

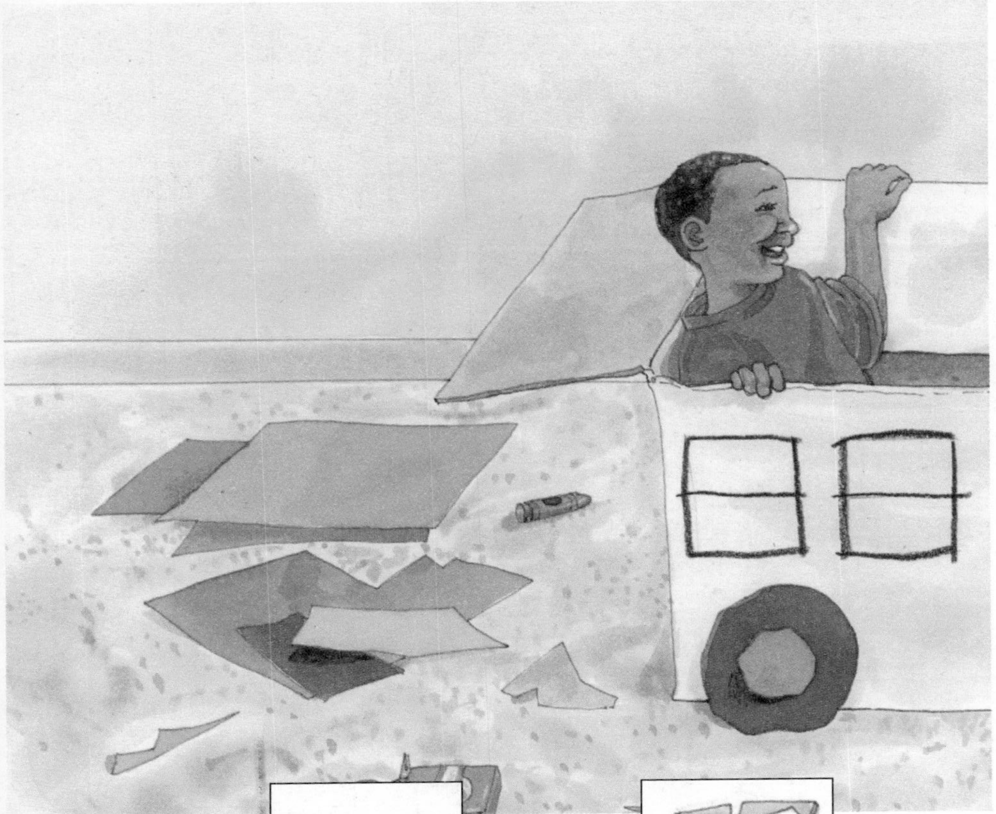

The 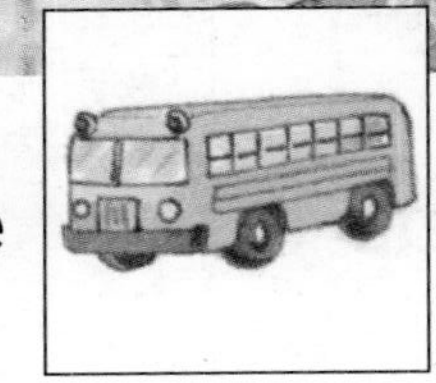

was a 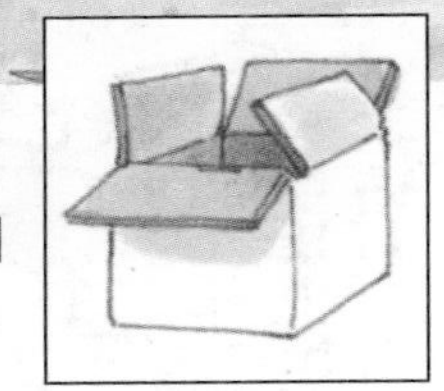

with 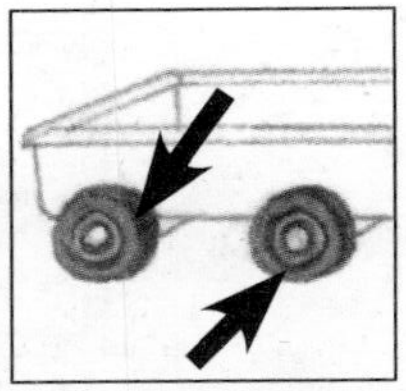

.

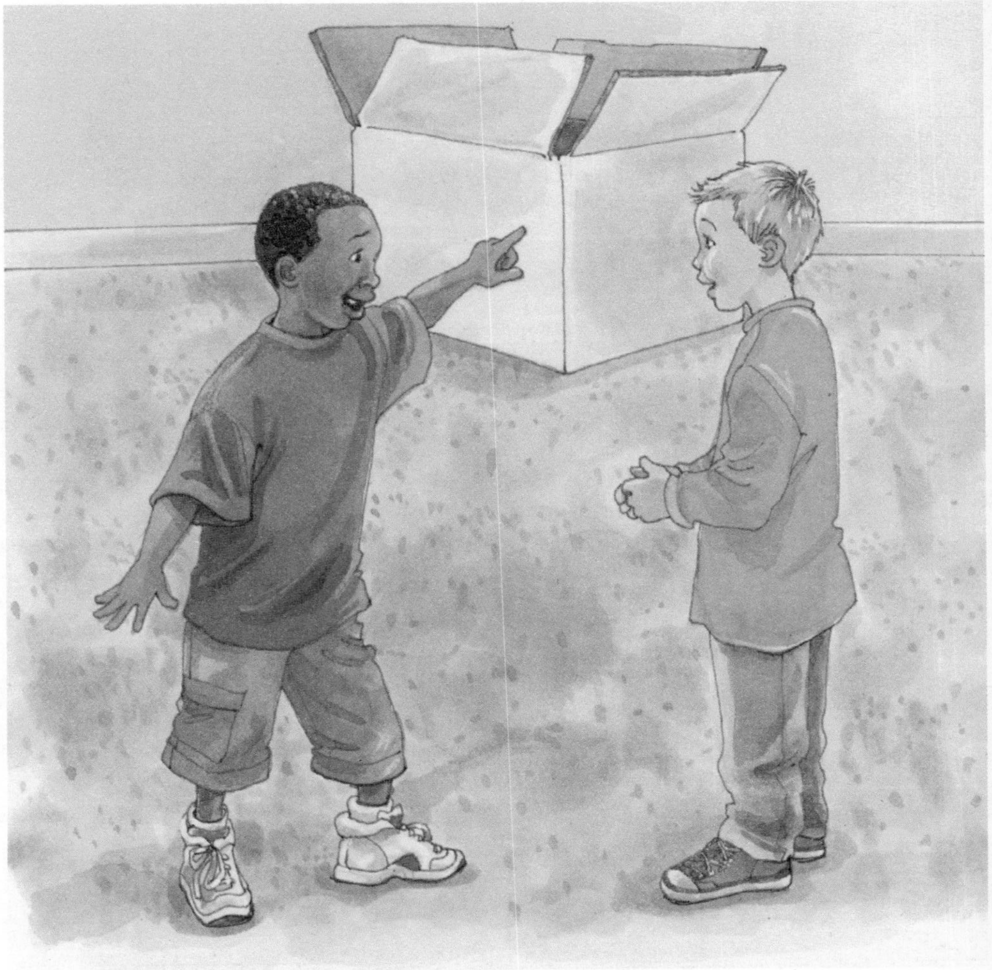

You and I have a 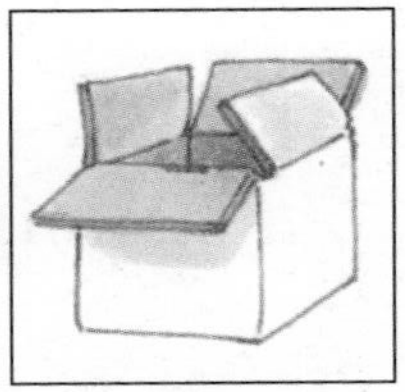

.

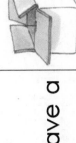

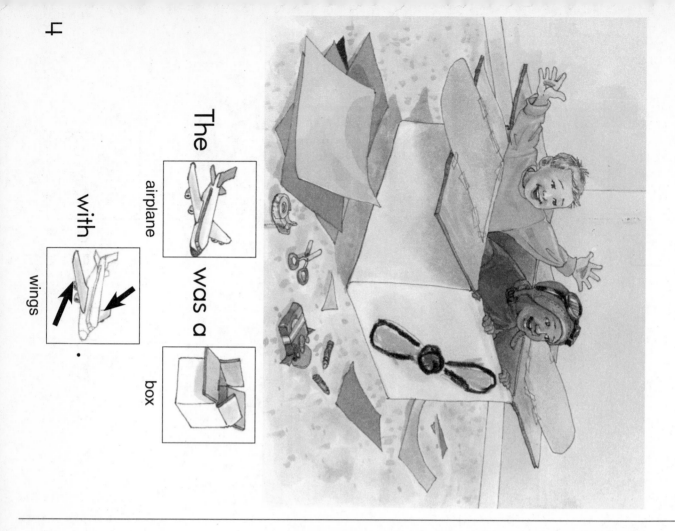

The [airplane] [box] was a

with [wings] .

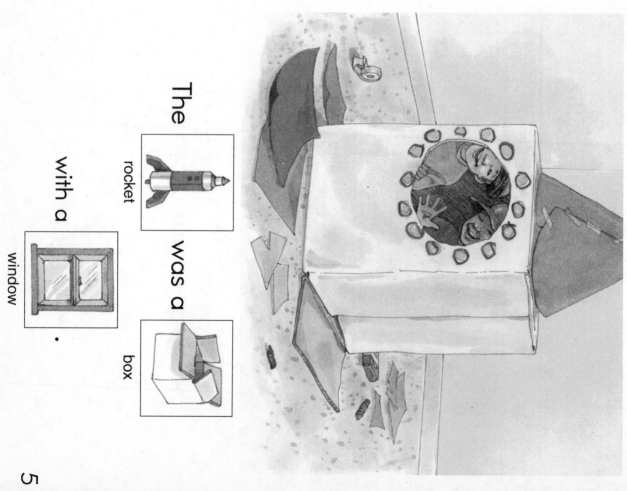

The [rocket] [box] was a

with a [window] .

SRA Pre-Decodables

The  Is Up

Farmer

by Vincent Zimmer
illustrated by Tom Leonard

Pre-Decodable 18

Mc Graw Hill **SRA**

Columbus, OH

77

The  is up with the 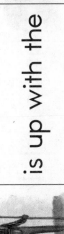 .

farmer

sheep

8

SRAonline.com

SRA
Mc Graw Hill

Send all inquiries to this address:
SRA/McGraw-Hill
4400 Easton Commons
Columbus, OH 43219

The *McGraw-Hill* Companies

The  is up with the .

dog

sheep

The  is up.

sun

The  is up on a  .

farmer   horse

4

The rooster is up on a 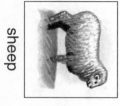 fence .

A  sheep is up on the 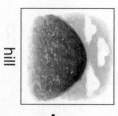 hill .

5

80

Down on the

Farm

by Tom Cunningham
illustrated by Alexandra Wallner

Pre-Decodable 19

SRA

Columbus, OH

81

The  go down a _____ .

ducks   path

SRAonline.com

Mc Graw Hill

SRA

The McGraw-Hill Companies

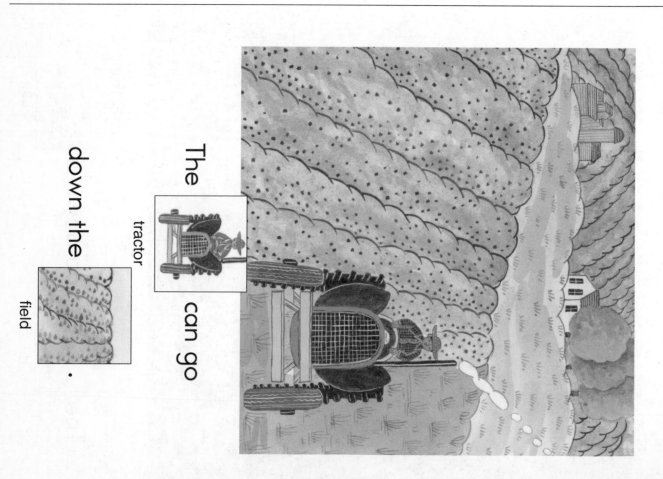

The

tractor

can go

down the

field

.

The  go down in 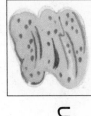 .

pigs

mud

3

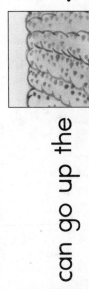

A  can go up the .

tractor

field

6

83

4

The 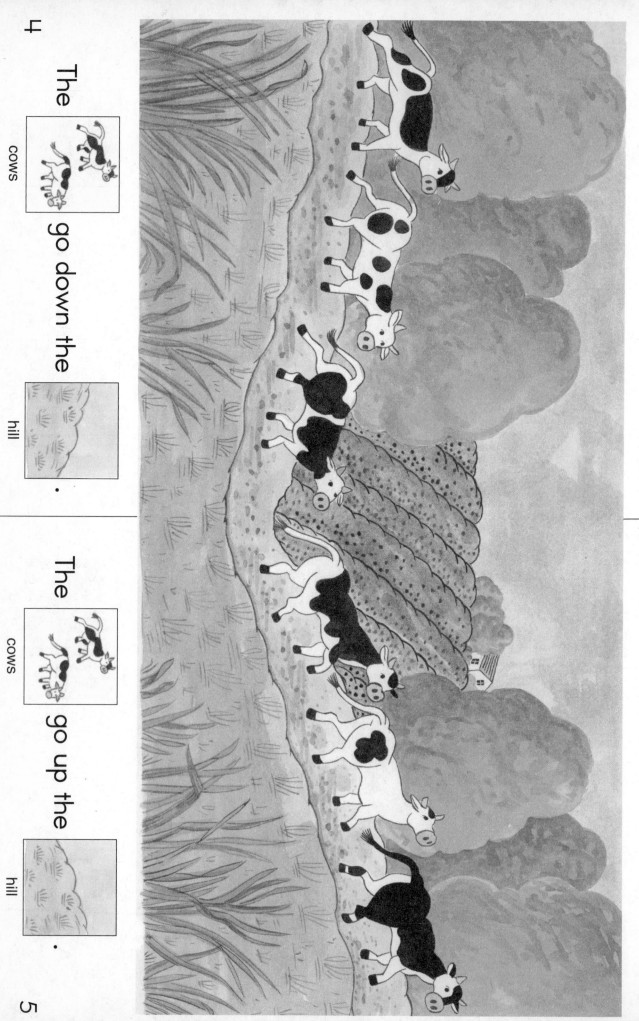 cows go down the 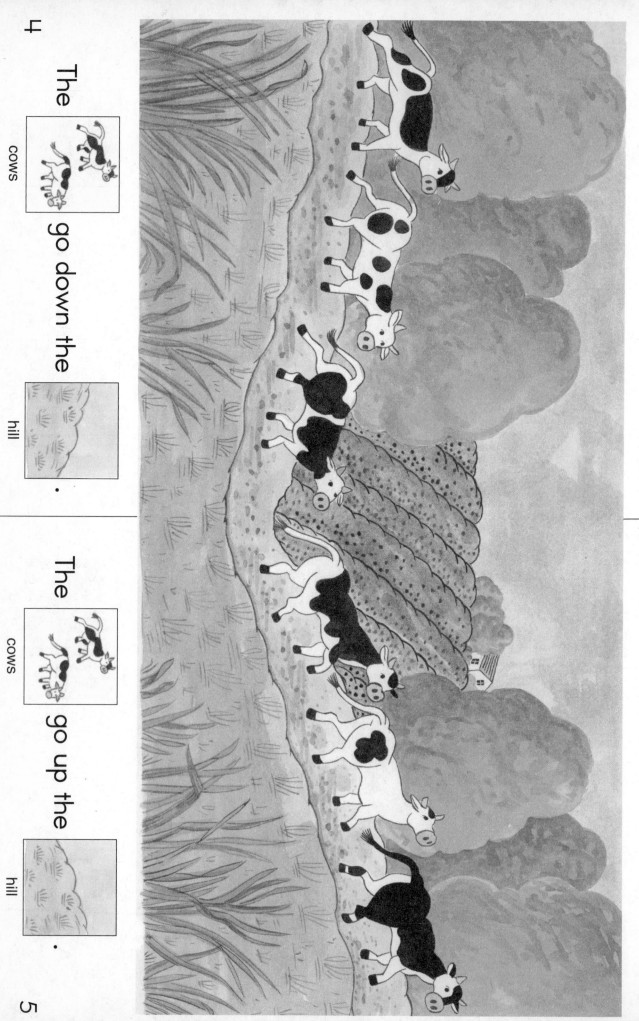 hill .

The 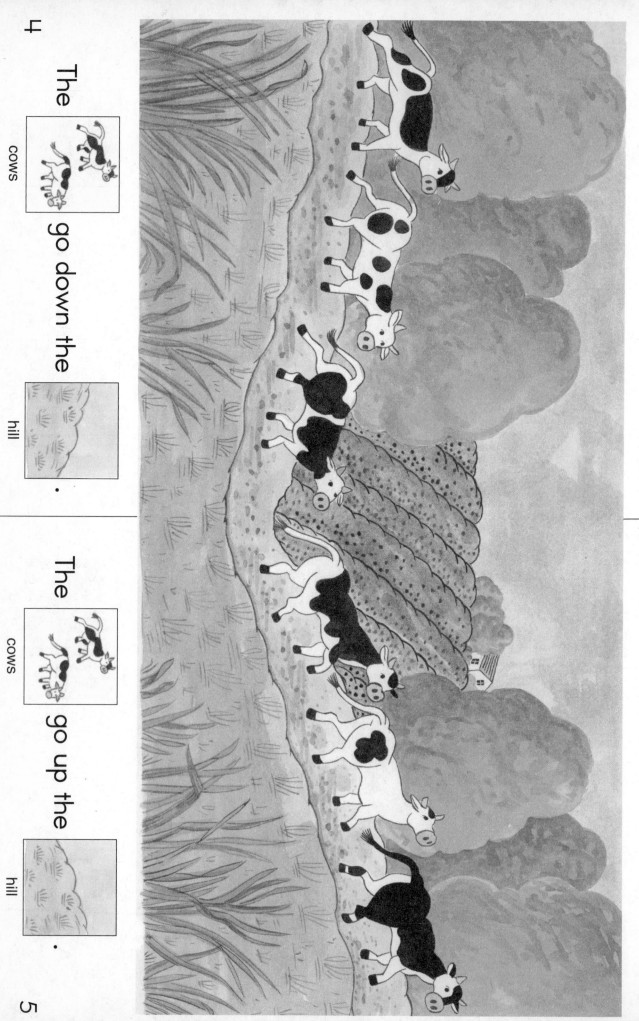 cows go up the 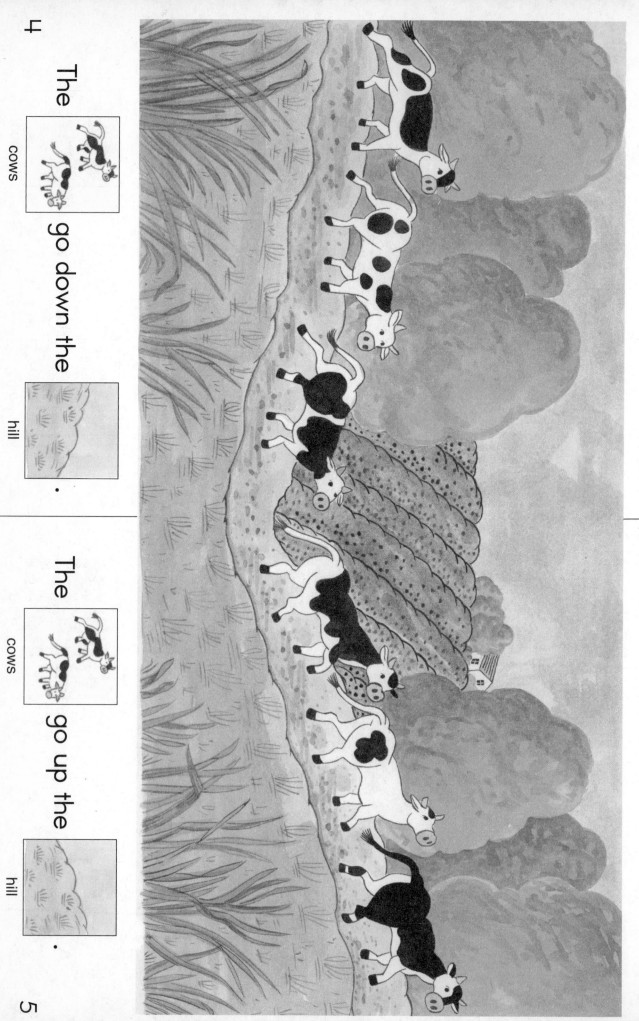 hill .

5

84

SRA Pre-Decodables

He Had a

Farm

by Rachel Bratter
illustrated by Meryl Henderson

Pre-Decodable 20

SRA

Columbus, OH

The farmer had a farm.

He had a   on the   .

barn

farm

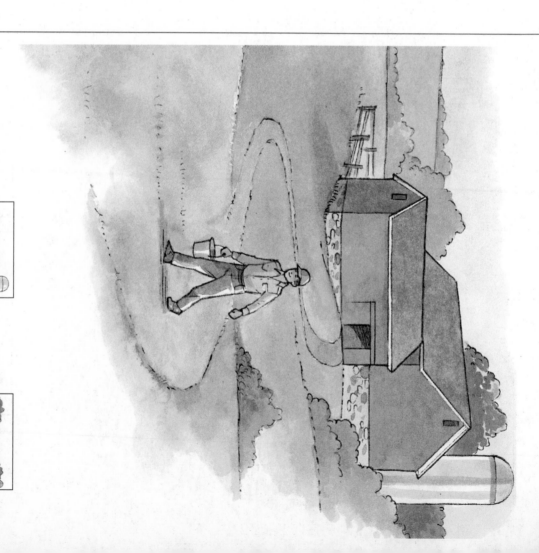

The  had a 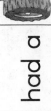 .

farmer   tractor

3

He had a  in the ___ .

horse   grass

6

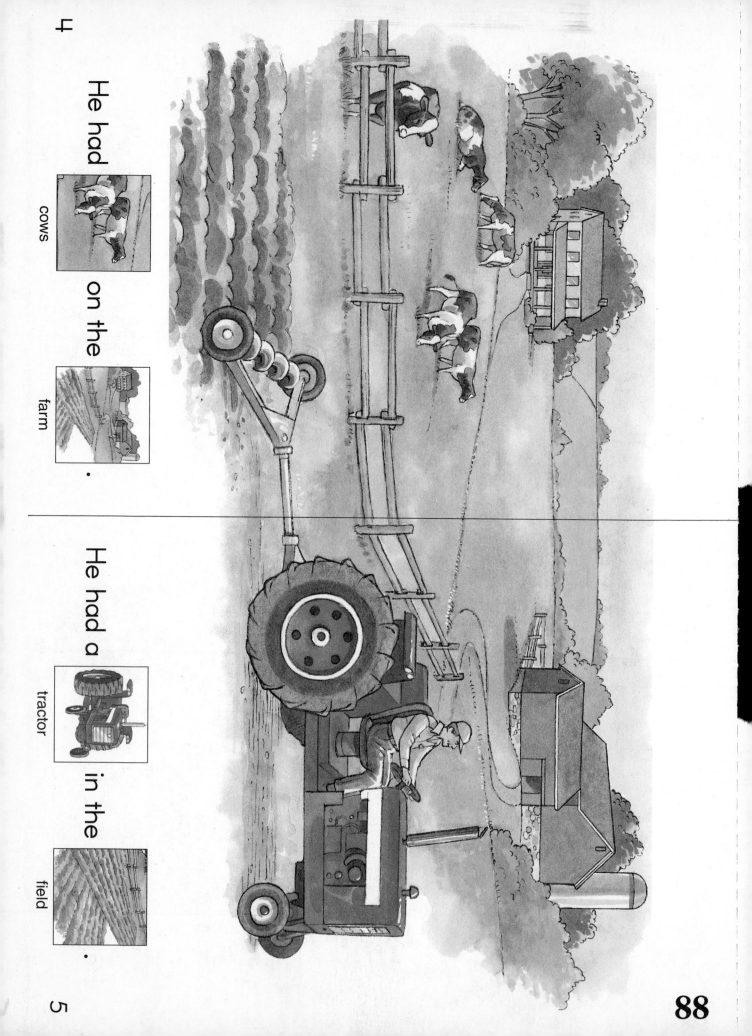

4   He had on the .

cows   farm

5   He had a in the .

tractor   field

88